ADVENTURES
with the GIANTS

by Catharine F. Sellew

ILLUSTRATED BY STEELE SAVAGE

Little, Brown and Company · *Boston*

Sixteenth Printing

*Published simultaneously
in Canada by McClelland and Stewart Limited*

PRINTED IN THE UNITED STATES OF AMERICA

By CATHARINE F. SELLEW

ADVENTURES *with the* GODS
ADVENTURES *with the* GIANTS
ADVENTURES *with the* HEROES

ADVENTURES
with the GIANTS

TO MY MOTHER and FATHER

About the Stories in This Book

THESE STORIES were first told many hundreds of years ago in the cold, cold lands of Northern Europe. Norsemen, as the people who lived in that North country were called, wanted to know what made the wind blow, what made things live and grow. The world seemed very different to them from the way it seems to us now. It was *so* long ago that they didn't know the facts about nature and science which we know today. So they tried to think up good reasons for the things that happened around them.

They would gather close to the fire, while the wind whistled outside, and tell stories — stories of the gods, giants and dwarfs, who, they thought, made everything happen in the world. And they would tell tales of exciting adventures in the struggle between the great gods and wicked giants.

The homes of the Norsemen were so close to the

North Pole that winter was the longest part of the year. Summer was warm but very short. There wasn't much time for flowers or vegetables to grow. The sun shone all day and even most of the night in the summertime. But in the long winter, night came too soon, making the days dark and dreary. So the men and women of the North had to fight against cold and darkness most of their lives. They had to brace themselves against howling winds, and climb icy cliffs. Their land was wild, with fierce and hungry beasts. It is easy to see why these men of the North had to be brave and strong.

In this book are some of the tales that the Norsemen told around their firesides. We still find their adventures exciting, and often their ideas can be found today in famous works of music, art and literature.

Some of their names may be difficult to read, but at the back of the book there is a list in the order of the alphabet. It will tell you what the names mean and how to say them.

Contents

CONTENTS

ADVENTURES
with the GIANTS

CHAPTER I

The Beginning of a World

LONG, LONG ago, before there were any days or nights — long before there was any time at all — there was no world: no earth or sky or sea. Only a deep crack yawned in the universe like the mouth of a huge monster. All around were mist and darkness. But deep down in the dark pit of the crack leaped the red tongue of fire.

There, too, a bottomless spring never stopped bubbling and running over. As the water rushed into the cold darkness it turned into sheets of ice. The great spirit looked down upon this ice and darkness. He saw that nothing grew there. He saw that all was gray and silent. So he made a tremendous man called a giant and placed him on the ice. He made a huge cow which gave the giant gallons and gallons of milk.

The huge cow used to feed on the salt she found in the ice. One day, while she was licking the salt, her

3

rough tongue came upon a golden hair. She licked and licked and found more golden hairs. Soon she found they were growing on the head of a giant frozen in the ice. Day after day she kept licking until she got to his shoulders, then his chest, then his waist. Finally he stood before her free from the ice. He was even taller and more handsome than her master. His name was Bure.

That was the beginning of a world of giants. It was a cold world with no sunshine, no blue sky, no green grass.

Some of the giants were evil, and they fought and quarreled with the good giants like Bure. Finally the grandsons of Bure conquered the bad giants and drove them far out into the cold gray twilight at the edge of the universe. It was so cold that their breath turned to ice the minute it passed their lips, and fell like icicles on the ground.

Then the children of the good giants made for themselves a new world in which they were to be the gods who ruled over all.

In the center of the universe they created a green land with rivers and lakes and mountains. That was the earth. Then they carved a man out of a tall

ash tree and a woman out of a graceful elm. The gods gave them the power to move and think. And they placed them on the earth to start the race of men.

At the top of the world the gods made a beautiful city for themselves. They called it Asgard. It was filled with gold and silver palaces. And because the gods wanted a road from their shining city down to the earth, and then down to the dark world of the giants, they took fire and water and air and made a wonderful rainbow. The rainbow was so wide and so strong and so long that it stretched like a bridge across the three parts of the universe.

Now there was a new world, but no sky to cover it. Where should the gods place the sun and the moon and the stars? Where should they place the fluffy white clouds or the heavy thunderheads? When they made the sky how should they hold it over the three parts of the world?

Finally they found four very strong and very ugly little men called dwarfs to hold the four corners of the sky on their shoulders. Their names were Nordri, Sudri, Austri and Westri, which mean North, South, East and West. And the gods filled the sky with sparks that shone when there was no sun or moon nearby. They called them stars.

In this new world there grew a mighty tree that was ever green. It was so tall that its topmost branches shaded the palaces of the gods and its lower branches shaded the earth and the land of the giants. The tree had three roots, one growing in each of the three parts of the world.

The ruler of this new world was All-father, king of the gods. He was a great warrior, and he called himself Odin. Odin's beautiful gray horse, Sleipner, had eight feet and could run faster than the wind. Sleipner carried his master through many fierce battles and on many long and dangerous adventures. And when the great All-father galloped across the rainbow bridge, the thundering of the horse's hoofs echoed from the heavens to the deepest and darkest caves of the giants.

CHAPTER II

How Odin Lost His Eye

ONCE when the world was still very young, Odin sat on his throne in the most beautiful palace in Asgard. His throne was so high that he could see over all three parts of the world from where he sat. On his head he wore a helmet shaped like an eagle. On his shoulders perched two black ravens called Memory and Thought. And at his feet crouched two snarling wolves.

The great king gazed thoughtfully down on the earth below him. He had made the green land that stretched out before his eyes. With the help of the other gods he had made men and women who lived on that earth. And he felt truly like the All-father he was called.

The fair elves had promised they would help his children of the earth. The elves were the tiny people who lived between heaven and earth. They were so small that they could flit about doing their work unseen. Odin knew that they were the artists who painted the flowers and made the beds for the streams. They took care of all the bees and the butterflies. And it was the elves who brought the gentle rain and sunshine to the earth.

Even the ugly dwarfs, who lived in the heart of the mountains, agreed to help. They forged iron and metals, made tools and weapons. They dug gold and silver and beautiful jewels out of the earth. Sometimes they even cut the grain and ground the flour for the farmers on the earth.

All seemed to be going well. Odin found it hard to think of evil times. But he knew that the frost giants were only waiting for a chance to bring trouble to his children. They were the ones who brought cold and ice to the world and shook the earth in anger. They hated Odin and all the work of the gods.

And from high on his throne Odin looked down beyond the earth deep into the gloomy land of his enemies. He saw dark figures of huge men moving about. They looked like evil shadows. He, the king of the gods, must have more wisdom. It was not enough just to see his enemies. He must know more about them.

So Odin wrapped his tall figure in a blue cloak. Down from his throne he climbed. Down the broad rainbow bridge he strode, and across the green earth till he came to one of the roots of the great ever green tree. There, close by the tree, was a well full of clear water. Its surface was so still it was like a mirror. In it one could see pictures of things that had happened and things that were going to happen.

But beside the well sat an old man. His face was lined with the troubles of the world. His name was Mimir, which means Memory. No one, not even the great Odin, could see the pictures in the well unless he first drank some of its water. Only Mimir could give the magic drink.

"Aged Mimir," Odin said to the old man, "you who hold the knowledge of the past and future in your magic waters, let me have but one sip. Then I can know enough to protect the men and women of the earth from the hate of the giants."

Mimir looked kindly at Odin, but he did not smile. Although he spoke softly, his voice was so deep it reminded Odin of the distant roar of the ocean.

"The price of one drink from this well is not cheap,"

Mimir said. "And once you have drunk and gazed into the mirror of life, you may wish you had not. For sorrow and death as well as joy are pictured there. Think again before you ask to drink."

But once the king of the gods had made up his mind nothing could change it. He was not afraid to look upon sorrow and death.

"What is your price, aged Mimir?" Odin asked.

"You are great and good, Odin," answered Mimir. "You have worked hard to make the world. Only those who know hard work may drink from my well. However, that is not enough. What have you given up that is very dear to you? What have you sacrificed? The price of a drink must be a great sacrifice. Are you still willing to pay the price?"

What could the king of the gods sacrifice? What was most dear to him? Odin thought of his handsome son, Balder, whom he loved most in the world. To give up his son would be like giving up life and all that was wonderful around him. Odin stood silent before Mimir. Indeed that would be a high price!

Then Mimir spoke again. He had read Odin's thoughts.

"No, I am not asking for your dear son. The Fates

say his life must be short, but he has time yet to live and bring happiness to the gods and the world. I ask for one of your eyes."

Odin put his hands up to his bright blue eyes. Those two eyes had gazed across the world from his high throne in the shining city of the gods. His eyes had taught him what was good and beautiful — what was evil and ugly. But those eyes had also seen his children, the men and women of the earth, struggling against the hate of the giants. One eye was a small sacrifice to win knowledge of how to help them. And without another thought, Odin plucked out one of his blue eyes and handed it to Mimir.

Then Mimir smiled and gave Odin a horn full of the waters of his well.

"Drink deeply, brave king, so you may see all that you wish in the mirror of life."

Odin lifted the horn to his lips and drank. Then he knelt by the edge of the well and watched the pictures passing across its still and silent surface. When he stood up again, he sighed, for it was as Mimir had said. He had seen sorrow and death as well as joy. It was only the glorious promise at the end, that gave him courage to go on.

15

So Odin, the great king of the gods, became one-eyed. If you can find Mimir's well, you will see Odin's blue eye resting on the bottom. It is there to remind men and women of the great sacrifice he made for them.

CHAPTER III

Frigga's Necklace

FRIGGA, the queen of the gods, sat beside Odin on the high throne on the top of the world. She was very beautiful, with white plumes in her hair that waved softly in the breeze. She wore snowy white robes and a golden girdle from which hung a ring of keys. She smiled down at the men and women of the earth and watched over their homes and children.

Often she feasted with the other gods and goddesses, but best of all she loved to spin golden thread and weave clouds of glowing colors to put in the sky. Her spinning wheel was set with jewels that sparkled at night. The people of the earth saw them shining in the sky and called them stars.

Frigga was kind and beautiful, but she was also very vain. She loved new gowns and bright jewelry. She could not be happy unless she was the most beautifully dressed goddess in Asgard.

One day she took out her box of jewels and looked at one necklace after another. None of them were quite brilliant enough or quite the right length. None of them really suited her new gown. She wanted a new necklace.

It should be a necklace of pure gold, she decided. It should be made in such a design that everyone — especially her husband, Odin — would wonder at it. So Frigga sent a messenger down to the workshop of the dwarfs. Those ugly little blacksmiths could make magic things out of the metals and jewels that they dug from the heart of the mountains.

Frigga's messenger went to the most skillful of the dwarfs, and told him what the queen of the gods wanted.

"It must be more beautiful than anything you have ever made," the messenger commanded.

"And all of gold?" asked the dwarf.

"Yes, pure gold. You must not use any other metal."

"But we do not have enough gold for such a necklace," said the dwarf, shaking his head sadly.

"Then dig deeper into the heart of the mountains until you have found enough. This is an order from Frigga! It is the goddess queen who demands it!"

"I know! I know! But we have already made many ornaments of gold for that beautiful lady and the other gods and goddesses. We have only a little gold left. Please explain this to her highness. Tell her I will make a necklace of wondrous beauty. It will be made of all the metals of the earth in a design worthy only of the lovely Frigga!"

When the messenger went back and told Frigga what the most skillful dwarf had said she was very disappointed. A necklace of many metals would no doubt be beautiful. But for her new gown — gold, pure gold, was needed. If the dwarfs could not get enough gold, *she* would find some on earth and send it to that most skillful dwarf.

Then the beautiful goddess put on her traveling robes and swept down the rainbow bridge. She walked for miles and miles over the earth in search of gold for her necklace. There was a gold ring here. There was a gold bracelet there. But they belonged to the men and women of the earth, whom Frigga loved as though they were her own children. She did not wish to take such things from them. Besides it would take many, many rings and bracelets to make enough gold.

At last she came to a statue that stood in a little village. It was much taller than any man of the earth. It shone so brightly that beams of light came from it and threw a dazzling glow for miles around. It was made of pure gold.

Frigga cried out with pleasure! Here at last was more than enough gold for her necklace. Just a small piece of the statue would be plenty. As the queen of the gods came closer, she saw it was a statue of her husband, Odin. It looked so much like Odin that for a minute she expected it to speak. She would not have been surprised if it had asked her what she was doing so far from her throne in Asgard.

But, no, it was only a dumb statue. She would just break off a piece of gold big enough for the necklace and no one would miss it. If it were missed, no one would know where it had gone. The dwarf would have already made it into a beautiful necklace for her.

The men and women of the earth had made this statue of the All-father so that they might worship him. Odin had been very pleased. He had been kind to those faithful men and women, and had protected them from the evil of the frost giants. In the dark of the night he often walked through the village and smiled upon the simple homes full of sleeping men and women. Even in the dark the gold statue glowed and threw a warm light upon the stones of the street.

It was on such a night that Odin discovered a piece of gold had been taken from his statue. He was very angry!

"What is this?" he shouted. "Who has dared to steal gold from my statue? He shall pay heavily for this. Do not think I am unable to discover the thief!"

Odin's voice rang through the silent village. Dark clouds rolled across the night sky. A fierce wind howled and tugged at the roofs of the little houses. And the men, women and children pulled their blankets over their heads and trembled with fear.

"The thief shall pay for this!" Odin roared again. The wind picked up his words and howled, "Thief! Thief!" And the giants in the dark cold depths of the earth laughed and shook their fists with joy. Evil was again in the world and the great Odin was angry.

Now the most skillful dwarf had already turned the stolen piece of gold into a necklace for Frigga. Never had there been such a handsome necklace. It had been hammered and twisted and carved in a way that immediately caught everyone's attention. All the goddesses gazed upon it with envy and wonder. Even Odin praised it.

"It is a thing of rare beauty," he had said. "Fit only for my queen to wear." And he had smiled upon Frigga and she was very happy.

But now Odin did not smile. He did not seem to notice Frigga or what she wore. He spoke seldom and sat upon his throne scowling down upon the earth. Nothing Frigga said or did could rouse him. She began to be afraid. What would happen if he ever found out she had stolen the gold?

Finally Odin went back to the statue. He wrote magic verses upon it so that the next morning it would be able to speak and name the thief.

When Frigga saw him writing upon the statue from her throne in Asgard, her face went white with terror. What could she do? Odin might never forgive her. Should she confess? No. His anger would be too terrible to bear. He must never know the truth. But how could she stop him from finding out?

Quickly, while Odin was still down on the earth, Frigga fled to the land of the dwarfs. Down the dark, winding underground passages she stumbled. Loose stones slipped under her feet and several times she

almost fell. Down and down she went until she came to the workshop of the blackest dwarf. The most skillful dwarf could not help her this time. The blackest dwarf must do the daring deed.

"Help me! Help me!" she begged as the tears ran down her pale cheeks. The little dwarf gazed at her in surprise. His face was grimy and red from working. His little green eyes gleamed with cunning. But his heart softened as he looked at the frightened goddess.

"What can I do?" he croaked. "I have no power against the great Odin."

"You must think of something," sobbed Frigga. "The statue will speak my name in the morning. Break the statue! You must break the statue!"

"I wouldn't dare," said the dwarf.

"Please! Please!" begged the goddess. And the great queen smiled through her tears upon the little black dwarf. "You are the only living creature who can help me. Is your heart hard and cold like the frost giants'? Will you leave me to face my husband's fearful rage, when by using your great cunning you can save me? Tell me you are not so cruel! Please destroy the statue!" Again Frigga wept.

"Well," said the blackest dwarf slowly, "perhaps I

can help you. I would not do such a thing for anyone else. I shall be taking a great chance."

"Surely you are not afraid to take a chance," Frigga said. She smiled at him and the rosy color came back into her cheeks. "I shall never forget your great kindness." Then she ran back up the dark passages and on up to her throne in Asgard.

The next morning Odin returned to the statue. Alas! It was broken into a million gold pieces scattered upon the ground. There was no longer any statue to speak the name of the thief. Odin stood looking down at the heap of gold with his one blue eye. As Frigga watched him from her throne, her heart stood still with fear. But Odin only stood there silently thinking. She could not see the black rage that darkened his brow, for his head was bent.

What was he thinking? Had he guessed now who the thief was? But how could he? What was he doing — standing there?

And then the great king of the gods turned on his heel. He did not look back. Without looking to the right or to the left he walked straight ahead until he disappeared from sight.

Days passed. Weeks passed. Months passed. Odin

did not return. Frigga sat alone on her high throne. The frost giants laughed with glee. Now who would rule the world and protect the people from evil? They blew cold blasts upon the earth. Storms raged on land and sea. The sun no longer warmed the world. Ice and snow covered everything.

In Asgard all was confusion and sadness. Odin had left the world. His silent anger was worse than any rage Frigga or the other gods and goddesses had ever known.

Frigga remembered the happy days before she had risked so much for the sake of vanity. The necklace no longer seemed beautiful. Because of it she had brought on all this evil and trouble. She knew that Odin had left the world because evil had been done, even though he might not have learned the name of the thief. She wept and prayed all night and all day for his forgiveness.

Then one day, when they had given up hope of ever seeing Odin again, the great All-father returned. He smiled upon Frigga and the other gods and goddesses. He looked down upon the dark, cold world. And, as he gazed, the ice began to melt. The sun began to break through the gray clouds. The plants began to grow. Odin was no longer angry. All was forgiven. The frost giants grumbled and growled, but there was nothing they could do.

Frigga never knew whether Odin had guessed the whole truth, but she never wore the beautiful gold necklace again.

CHAPTER IV

Sif's Golden Hair

WHEN THE SKY grew black and the thunder growled and the lightning flashed, the people of the North used to say that Thor was driving his chariot across the heavens. Thor was one of Odin's sons. When he was only a baby, he lifted and tossed aside ten loads of bearskins. Odin and Frigga knew then that their son was to be one of the heroes of Asgard.

Thor grew up to be the largest and strongest of the gods. He had bright red hair and a bushy red beard that flashed sparks when he was angry. Great muscles bulged in his arms. No wonder he was named the thunder god!

Thor was much too heavy for a horse to carry. He rode in a chariot pulled by two goats called Tooth-cracker and Toothgnasher. And he was forbidden to pass over the rainbow bridge. The bridge had been built so that it would not hold the weight of a giant.

The gods were afraid that it would not hold Thor, either, and that the heat from his fiery red hair would destroy it. So Thor was forced to drive through cold rivers of mist to join the council of the gods by the fountain at the foot of the ever green tree.

Now Thor had a very beautiful wife called Sif. One reason for Sif's beauty was her golden hair. It fell in wonderful gleaming waves from the top of her head all the way to the ground, so that she seemed to be covered by a gorgeous golden veil. Thor was very proud of his wife's beautiful hair.

But one morning Thor wakened and leaned over to kiss his wife good morning. Alas! Sif's golden hair was gone! Thor rubbed his eyes. He must be dreaming! No, there lay his beautiful wife with all her hair cut off. Her head was white and bare.

"Sif! Sif!" Thor shook his wife awake. "What have you done?"

Sif opened her blue eyes in surprise. She was not used to being so rudely awakened.

"What's the matter?" she murmured.

"Your hair! Where is your hair?"

"My hair?" Sif put her hands up to her head. She felt the roughness where her hair had been cut. "Thor!

Thor! What has happened?" Sif hid her head under the bearskin on the bed. "My hair has been cut off! My beauty is gone. I'll be ugly for the rest of my life!"

Thor tried to comfort her, but he was so upset and angry he did not know what to say. Who could have done such a thing? Surely no one in Asgard hated Sif. Yet why should anyone cut off her hair unless it was because of jealous hatred? Maybe it was a poor kind of joke.

A joke! A wicked joke! Thor jumped up from the bed where Sif lay sobbing.

"It is that evil Loki who has done this to you!" he cried. "No other in Asgard would want to do this wicked thing."

Loki, the fire god, was a mischief-maker. He loved to make trouble wherever he went. He liked to see people get excited over things he had done secretly. He was very handsome and looked so gay and friendly that usually no one suspected him.

But Thor knew better. Out of the door he went, shouting great oaths that echoed like thunder all over the world. Sparks flew from his hair and beard. And the earth shook under his angry step.

Odin, the All-father, heard Thor shouting. And

when he heard what had happened to Sif's golden hair, he, too, thought of Loki.

"Find him," Odin called after Thor. "And if he *did* cut off Sif's hair, punish him. But remember to be fair. Do not let your temper control you!"

Loki, far away, heard those words and trembled. Thor's anger was greatly to be feared. But when the All-father was angry, too, there was even more reason to be afraid. So he ran as fast as he could.

Thor soon caught up to him. Loki quickly changed himself into a horse and raced ahead, but this did not fool Thor, who ran close behind. Then Loki turned himself into a fish and leaped into a river. Thor pulled a fish net out of his pocket, and soon Loki was flip-flopping helplessly in it. When Thor's big fist closed around the fish, Loki turned himself back to his real form. He tried to speak and plead forgiveness, but Thor's hands were closing around his throat.

Just in time, Thor remembered Odin's words — "Be fair." Thor did not *know,* he had only guessed Loki was guilty. He loosened his iron grip.

"Forgive me," gasped the mischief-maker. "I will get Sif a new head of hair! Let me go, and I will make up for my wrong."

32

"So you *did* cut off her hair!" thundered Thor. His hands grabbed again at Loki's throat.

"Stop! Let me go! Unless you allow me to live, Sif will never be beautiful again."

"How soon will you get her a new head of hair?" snapped Thor. "She cannot show herself before the gods and goddesses until she has her hair."

"Before the daylight is gone, Sif will have a new head of hair," promised Loki. "It will be as long and as beautiful as ever."

Thor paused. "Very well," he agreed at last. "But if you do not come back before evening with the golden hair for my dear wife, I will break every bone in your body!"

Then the great thunder god returned to his palace to tell poor Sif of Loki's promise.

CHAPTER V

The Magic Gifts

LOKI watched the angry thunder god disappear in the distance. He sighed with relief, and rubbed his swollen throat where Thor's hands had nearly choked him. But he must get busy. It was almost noon. Daylight was half gone. There was much to be done before the shadow of night's chariot crossed the sky.

He must find a head of hair as beautiful as the locks he had cut from Sif's head. Loki reached into his pocket. Silky threads of gold spilled out into the light. It was Sif's hair! The sunshine fell on it and flashed back with such brightness that Loki closed his eyes. Then he turned and went into a cave in the side of a mountain. This was the shortest way to the home of the dwarfs.

Loki ran swiftly down the long winding tunnels. Dead leaves rustled under his feet. The air smelled of wet earth. He had to bend his shoulders to keep from hitting his head on the rough ceiling. The dwarfs called out to him as he passed, for Loki was well known in this land of magic. Their green eyes shone in the darkness. How ugly they are, thought Loki, like strange small animals, with their little bodies, big heads and pointed ears. Their feet seemed like those of crows. And their faces were always a dirty gray, no matter how hard they scrubbed them. Luckily they were never allowed outside their mountain while day still lit the earth.

Once a bold dwarf had stepped out into the warm sunshine. Lo, he was instantly turned to stone!

A faint light flickered through the darkness, growing brighter and brighter as Loki drew closer. Voices and the clash of metal echoed in the passageway. He could hear the roar of the bellows that blew the flames hotter. At last he came out into a brightly lit cave. In the corners were huge piles of shining metals and glittering jewels. In the center beside the stone hearth and anvil stood a dwarf called Dvalin. Beads of sweat covered his wrinkled forehead as he worked before the hot fire. He turned when he heard Loki call out.

"Ah, Loki, what mischief are you up to now?" Dvalin asked with a grin.

"I'm in trouble," answered the god.

"Again?" chuckled the dwarf.

"Speak to me with respect," Loki cried angrily. "You forget I am a god."

"I beg your pardon," and Dvalin turned back to his work. He knew this handsome god needed his help. Loki could not put on airs with him. But he rather liked the young mischief-maker just the same.

"You must make me a head of hair as beautiful as this." Loki tossed Sif's locks in a heap on the floor of the cave. In the firelight the hair gleamed like the metal the dwarfs dug from the heart of the mountains. "And it must grow into the head of the goddess and become alive. I must have it before the daylight on the earth is gone."

"You are a devil!" muttered the dwarf. He looked thoughtfully at the mass of hair on the floor and scratched behind his pointed ear.

"Come, come," teased Loki. "Don't tell me your magic can't make a head of hair!" But he was worried. What could he do if Dvalin failed him?

"Well," the dwarf said slowly, "perhaps I can do what you want."

"Good!" cried Loki. He sat down on a three-legged

stool and prepared to wait. Dvalin scurried around the cave. He took three handfuls of crushed buttercups which he had picked in a field by moonlight. He added three cups of dew that sparkled like diamonds, a lump of rich gold metal, and a pinch of magic powder. All these he stirred together in a big black pot. Then he called his helpers to build up the fire. Loki watched lazily, thinking of all that had happened that morning.

"Dvalin," he called suddenly. The dwarf was busy with his work and only nodded his head in answer. "Odin was very angry with me. If I had a wonderful gift for him, he might forget my mischief. Surely you could make the All-father some useful present with your great magic?"

"You ask a great deal," Dvalin called over his shoulder.

"You will be well repaid. I will make you known as the most skillful dwarf in all the world."

Dvalin smiled. "I'll see what I can do," he said. And he shouted down the passageways for more help. Dwarfs scuttled into the cave from all directions. Some dropped down from the walls where they had been sleeping in the hollows of the rock. Some crept out from behind the pile of jewels which they had been counting. Some came in dragging picks and shovels.

Then what a clamor of voices and ringing metal! The fire blazed brighter. The cave grew hotter and hotter.

As time passed, Loki began to worry again. It was so dark far down under the earth that he could not tell whether the sun were still in the sky.

"Hurry! Hurry!" he called, but the busy dwarfs did not hear him. Already the shadows of night might cover the earth! Already Loki's punishment might have been decided by the gods! The young god jumped to his feet and looked into the tunnel that led to the top of the earth. Of course all he could see was inky blackness. Then Dvalin called him.

"What do you think of this?" he asked, his face shining with pride. He took the sharp point of a spear from the glowing coals. "Give this to the All-father. Tell him to fasten it to the end of the branch he cut from the ever green tree. He will then have a spear which will never miss its aim. And any man or god who swears an oath upon its point will never be able to break his word."

"Wonderful! Wonderful!" exclaimed Loki. "But Sif's hair . . ."

"And look at this," cried Dvalin. He took something small that one of the dwarfs held out to him. When he unfolded it, it looked like a tiny boat. Then the dwarfs took hold of each end and pulled and pulled. It grew larger and larger until it filled half the cave.

"You can make it even larger," explained Dvalin. "It will hold all the gods in Asgard and all their horses. It will sail in the air as well as on water. And yet it can be folded up and put in your pocket." And — whisk — the boat was all rolled up and handed to Loki!

"Marvelous!" gasped Loki. "But the golden hair . . ." None of these other things would save him if he returned without the golden hair.

"Oh, the golden hair," smiled Dvalin. "You look out for yourself, don't you? No, I haven't forgotten the golden hair." And he took an armful of shimmering gold from another dwarf. It was even more wonderful than the hair that Loki had cut from Sif's head. Dvalin had spun it from the magic mixture he had made in the black pot. He assured Loki that the minute it touched Sif's head it would grow just like real hair.

Loki quickly thanked Dvalin and tucked the three magic gifts under his cloak. "Your name will be famous all over the world," he called over his shoulder, and dashed into the dark passageway that led to the top of the earth.

As Loki burst out of the side of the mountain, day was just disappearing into the river of mist. He was not too late. In triumph he entered Thor's palace, heedless of new troubles awaiting him as they wait for all mischief-makers.

CHAPTER VI

The Dwarfs' Contest

ALL THE GODS were waiting for Loki to return from the land of the dwarfs. It grew so late that they began to fear he would fail to carry out his promise to the thunder god. But when they saw him leap out of the mountain with a gay smile on his face, they knew Sif was to have her new hair. But would it be as beautiful as the locks Loki had cut?

The last moments of daylight lit the sky. All Asgard watched Loki hold the new hair against poor Sif's head. There it grew fast, a shimmering veil as lovely as ever! Some said it was even more beautiful. Tears of joy rolled down Sif's cheeks and she ran happily to Thor, her husband.

Then Loki proudly gave the spear and the magic boat to Odin.

"How wonderful!" gasped the gods. "Who made these magic things? How did you persuade a dwarf to make them for you?" Loki was stormed with questions. The gods — even the great All-father — forgot what a mischief-maker he was.

"The master craftsman," said Loki when the questions had stopped, "is none other than the dwarf Dvalin. I declare him the most clever and skillful of all blacksmiths!"

The gods clapped their hands and shouted Dvalin's name so loudly that the ugly dwarf could hear it deep down in the heart of the mountain. He smiled happily. It was indeed a great reward to have all the gods give him such high praise.

But then the gods heard a harsh cry:

"That's not true! You dare not say that Dvalin is most skillful! Everyone knows my brother, the dwarf Sindri, is the greatest blacksmith! Loki lies! Loki lies!"

There stood an ugly black dwarf whom the gods knew to be Brock, brother of the clever Sindri. The sun had long ago disappeared, and Brock had crawled out onto the earth, as the little creatures within the mountains sometimes did after dark.

The gods looked with surprise at the angry dwarf. He was jumping up and down with rage, and shaking his hairy fists at Loki. His brows were knitted together

46

in a terrible black scowl. His green eyes gleamed with hatred.

"You dare boast of that stupid Dvalin! I will make you pay for the mischief you have been making ever since you were born!" screamed Brock. Loki laughed in the dwarf's face.

"The dwarf who made these magic gifts could not be stupid. You are jealous."

"That's enough, Loki," Odin spoke up in his deep voice. He looked kindly at Brock. "It is true that before this we have said that your brother, Sindri, was the greatest blacksmith. But Sif's hair and my spear and marvelous boat are the most wonderful magic we have yet seen."

"Great All-father," answered Brock with bowed head, "Sindri will make three things that you and all the other gods will declare more wonderful than any of those."

"Ha!" laughed Loki. "Wait till old Sindri hears that! You *have* got him in a fix now! I'll wager my own head that he cannot do such a thing."

Brock smiled, showing his pointed yellow teeth. "Great All-father, honored gods, you have heard what Loki said?" he asked.

"We have heard," they all answered. And Brock disappeared as quickly as he had come.

Down in the heart of the mountain, Brock went to his brother's workshop. He told him what Loki had said and the wager he had made. Sindri sat for a long time thinking.

"You expect much of me, Brother," he said at last. "Dvalin is not stupid. The things he made are truly wonderful."

"Ah! But you can do better — far, far better!" cried the faithful Brock. "I will gladly blow the fire with the bellows."

"Very well. I will do my best," replied Sindri. "But you must never stop the bellows. Not even for a second, for the fire must burn at an even heat."

So Brock crouched by the fire and worked the bellows. The coals turned from red to yellow and finally to a white heat. Then Sindri threw a lump of gold into the leaping flames, and crouched in the darkest corner of the cave. There he muttered secret words to the hidden powers of magic.

Meanwhile a huge horsefly buzzed into the cave. Round and round Brock's head it flew. When he shook his head to try to scare the fly away, it only flew closer and closer. Brock had never seen such a big horsefly. Suddenly it landed on his hand and stung him. It hurt dreadfully — much more than any ordinary horsefly sting — but Brock did not let go of the bellows. He kept the fire at a steady heat even as the bite swelled and turned purple.

At last Sindri stopped muttering and came out of the corner. "You can stop now," he said as he lifted the lump of gold from the fire with a pair of tongs. And lo, the shapeless lump had become a huge wild boar with golden bristles!

"The god of sunshine can drive this boar across the sky. Sunshine will flash from its bristles and light the world!" exclaimed Sindri.

"Wonderful! Wonderful!" chuckled Brock as he rubbed his swollen hand. "But we must keep on with our work." And he picked up the bellows and turned again to the fire.

Again Sindri tossed a lump of gold on the fire and went off to his dark corner. And again the huge horsefly buzzed into the cave and around Brock's head. Its buzzing rang in the dwarf's ear and made him feel dizzy. In the bright light of the fire the fly seemed to

51

be a black spot dancing before Brock's eyes, trying to blind him.

"You must be sent by the devil," Brock shouted angrily. "In fact," he added with a sudden thought, "I wouldn't be surprised if you *were* that devil Loki!"

At that the horsefly stung the dwarf cruelly on the cheek. The pain shot across his face and almost stunned him. But Brock held firmly to the bellows and the fire roared. Would Sindri never come back to the fire? Brock gritted his teeth.

Finally Sindri returned. This time he pulled a gold ring from the fire. It was as big as a bracelet, but perfectly plain. Brock was puzzled.

"What is this, Brother?"

"Ah, Brock, you are disappointed. Don't be. This is a *magic* ring. This you will give to Odin. Every ninth night, eight rings, exactly like this one, will drop from it. It means that Odin will have many beautiful children. It means that there will always be people in the world."

Brock was pleased, but he thought to himself, "These gifts are wonderful, but so are Dvalin's. The third must be even better!" Yet Sindri smiled with satisfaction as he told Brock to blow up the fire. This time he threw a lump of iron upon the flames.

The fire curled its flaming tongue around the dark metal. It threw snaky shadows on the walls of the cave. The shadow of Brock blowing the bellows seemed to grow on all sides. The only sounds in the cave besides Sindri's low muttering were the crackle of the flames and the *sush* of the air from the bellows.

Had the horsefly gone? Brock was sure now that it had been Loki. Had he given up so soon? Or did he think the gifts were so poor that there was no need to try to ruin Sindri's work? Ah no! The loud buzzing sounded again, and the huge horsefly sped out of the darkness straight at Brock's face, stinging him in the eye.

Brock cried out with pain, but he kept at the bellows. The fire was terribly hot, and the air in the room seemed stifling. Poor Brock could feel the blood flow into his eyes! It ran down his cheek. His head was spinning and he could hardly see, but he must keep the fire hot. He could hear Sindri muttering and muttering. He dared not call to him for fear he would break the spell. He must wipe the sticky blood from his face or soon he would be unable to see at all.

53

Quickly — ever so quickly — he stopped the bellows just long enough to brush his hand across his face. But it was not quick enough. Sindri rushed from his corner.

"What have you done? Why did you stop? Did I not tell you what would happen? All my work . . ." And he grabbed up the tongs and anxiously pulled the iron from the fire. Then he smiled as he held up a huge hammer with a queer short handle.

"All is well," he said. "The handle is a little short because the fire died down for a moment. But that makes little difference. This you will give to the thunder god, Thor. Only he is strong enough to hurl it. It will destroy the enemies of the gods. And after Thor has thrown it, back it will fly to his hand so that he will never have to go after it."

"Ah, Sindri," smiled Brock. "This gift is the greatest of all. We will have Loki's head for this!" And he put the golden boar, and the magic ring and the great hammer on a sledge and dragged them up out of the mountain to present them to the gods.

It was just as Brock had said. The gods were pleased with the wonderful boar. The ring was indeed a thing of magic. But so were Dvalin's gifts. And then Brock, with all his strength, lifted the great hammer and gave it to Thor. It was not a thing of beauty. But what a weapon it was for the gods! That hammer might win the war against the giants. No gift of Dvalin's gave the gods such power.

"Yes, Brock," said Odin, "your brother is a great blacksmith. Because of this hammer he shall be known as the greatest blacksmith in the world!"

"And Loki will pay his bet?" Brock could still feel the pain from the stings of the horsefly.

"Ah," spoke up Loki hastily. "It was all in fun, good Brock."

"It was a wager," answered Brock firmly. "It was made before all the gods."

"That is so," agreed the great All-father a little sadly, for he did not like to see those in Asgard suffer. However, a god always kept his word.

But Loki laughed. "You may have my head," he said. "I guess it is rightfully yours, but you cannot touch my neck!" And how could Brock cut off Loki's head without touching his neck? Clever Loki! Brock stormed with anger, but the gods agreed that what Loki said was true.

"Then, since your head is mine," cried Brock angrily

"I shall get Sindri's needle and sew up your lips so your evil words can no longer make trouble in this world."

The gods agreed that Loki would have to permit this. Loki had so often told lies just to stir up excitement. He had so often talked his way out of fair punishment. So often his smooth words had won him friends who never dreamed he was really a troublemaker. Indeed, the gods were not sorry to see that quick tongue stilled!

Loki knew this would be hard punishment. It would not be easy to enjoy life with his lips sealed. He would no longer be able to persuade gods and giants — or even dwarfs — to do as he wished.

But when Brock returned with Sindri's needle, Loki had to let him sew those telltale lips together. Then the gods returned to their palaces in Asgard. They were sad that one of them must suffer, but Loki had made an agreement and they knew that he should live up to it.

CHAPTER VII

Thor's Voyage
to the Land of the Giants

NOW that Loki could no longer laugh and joke, Asgard seemed very dull and quiet. The gods missed their gay companion. But they reminded themselves that no mischief had been done since Brock had sewed up Loki's lips. That was indeed a good thing.

Even Thor felt sorry for Loki as he passed him walking slowly and silently through the streets. Perhaps this would teach the young fire god a lesson. Thor knew that it would not be long before Loki found a way to cut Brock's stitches. Then he would be his merry self again.

So it happened. One morning Loki's laughter rang out in the city of the gods, and he pranced before them. His lips were still thick and swollen, but Brock's stitches were gone!

Since Thor had received Sindri's magic hammer, he

had been anxious to go to the land of the giants. He would show those wicked rulers of ice and darkness how great and powerful were the gods! But he wanted a brave and daring companion. He thought of Loki, whose punishment seemed to have made him eager to please others. In fact, Loki seemed to have forgotten his love of mischief.

"Will you come with me?" Thor asked him after explaining his plan. "But no mischief, mind you!" he thundered.

"Mischief!" cried Loki. "How can you think of such a thing? Haven't I been punished enough for my jokes? But Asgard is dull these days. I want adventure!"

"Very well," agreed Thor. "See that you don't try any of your old tricks."

So they set out on their long journey to the land of the giants. Thor's two strong goats pulled the chariot swiftly through the gates of Asgard. The gods cheered and waved to them as they raced out of sight.

Thor's great hammer was carefully fastened to his magic belt. Whenever he needed extra strength, all he had to do was to pull this belt tighter about his waist. And he wore thick gloves to protect his hands from the heat of the hammer. Loki leaned back in his seat while Thor held the reins. He enjoyed the feel of the bright sunshine and the wind whistling through his hair.

Thus they traveled swiftly all day. By the time the sun had disappeared behind black mountains, they reached the edge of the land of the giants. Before them was a tiny cottage where a poor peasant family lived. They stopped there, and the peasants welcomed the great red-bearded man and his handsome friend.

"We have very little to offer," said the father, "but we are glad to share it with you." And the mother set a small cheese and a loaf of barley bread on the table. Loki's eyes twinkled as he looked at Thor. He knew the great thunder god could swallow it all in one gulp, and hardly know he'd eaten it! Thor laughed and said that he would provide the meat. Whereupon he killed his two goats and added them to the meal. The peasants gasped with wonder.

"Eat all you wish," roared Thor, "but see that you don't break any of the bones. When you have eaten all the meat off them, throw them on the goats' skins over there."

The peasants and their two children ate hungrily, and threw aside the bones as Thor had commanded.

Now Loki had been good for so long that he felt he simply must play a joke. One little harmless joke he could chuckle over in the old happy way! So, in spite of the warning Thor had given him before they set out on their journey, he leaned over and whispered to the peasants' son, "It's a shame, not to taste the good paste in the center of the bone! It is the most delicious part of the goat. Why don't you break a small bone and try it? No one will ever know." And he smiled at the boy. As long as the red-bearded man's friend had suggested it, the boy saw no harm in trying it. He did what Loki said. Indeed the marrow was good!

The next morning, when Thor woke, he waved his hammer over the skins upon which the bare bones lay. Up sprang the goats alive again, ready to pull the chariot. But, alas, one of them had a slight limp.

"Someone disobeyed my orders," thundered Thor, angry sparks flying from his red beard. The peasants trembled, for they realized now that their guests were gods. The son, who was called Thialfi, fell upon his knees. He told what he had done and begged forgiveness. Thor glared at Loki.

"I should have known I could not trust you!" he muttered. Then he turned to the boy. "Evil thoughts were put into your head," he said kindly, "so you are not altogether to blame. To win forgiveness you and your sister, Roskva, must come with us and be our servants. We will leave my goats in the care of your father and mother. Come! We must be on our way." And he led them out of the door before the peasants could thank him for his kindness.

All the next day they traveled on foot. Finally they came to a great sea. It was cold and gray, with angry waves pounding against the shore. The gods told the peasant children to follow them and not to be afraid. Then they waded into the rough sea and began to swim. Thialfi and Roskva took a deep breath and followed. Lo! It was as easy to swim as in their quiet pond at home, for they were traveling with gods.

Finally the swimmers pulled themselves up on a strange shore. The mist over this land was so thick that they could not guess what hour it was. But Thor declared it was time to look for a place to rest for the night. So they went ahead very slowly feeling with their hands and feet. Thialfi cried out as he felt something cold and wet and soft in front of him. When the

61

others came to help, they discovered it was only wet moss on the side of a great boulder.

"Look ahead!" cried the thunder god. He pointed to a dark mass that loomed in the mist. As they came closer it looked like a strangely shaped house. The doorway filled one side and was wide open. An odd tower went off at a queer angle.

Carefully they tiptoed inside. There was no fire — no hearth upon which to place great logs. The house was quite empty, without furniture, yet it seemed safe enough. At least it was shelter from the wet, cold mist. The travelers threw themselves on the floor and soon fell fast asleep.

After a while Roskva woke with a start. Her teeth were chattering. No, the ground was trembling! The whole strange house was shaking. She could hear a dull rumbling and roaring. Then all was still for a moment, only to begin again as though the whole world were shuddering.

"Thialfi! Thialfi!" Roskva whispered and reached out in the darkness for her brother's hand. Thialfi was sitting up, too. Then Thor and Loki felt their way over to the children. No one knew what was happening. Whatever it was, the strange house did not appear to be tumbling down on top of them. It did not seem to do any harm. Finally it seemed to stop.

"I saw a small room off this great hall," said Thor. "The three of you finish the night in there. I will guard the doorway till morning." So they went to the little room and soon fell asleep again.

Next morning Thor's loud laughing woke them.

"Well, I found out about the earthquake last night," he chuckled. And he grinned down at them while they sat up and rubbed their eyes. "You know what this palace is?"

They shook their heads. Loki jumped to his feet. He was a little ashamed of having been frightened last night, now that Thor seemed to think it all such a joke.

"You've been sleeping in the thumb of a giant's mitten!" Thor threw back his head and roared with good humor. "The giant was sleeping just outside!"

"Oh!" cried Roskva with a little scream.

"The earthquake was his snoring! There's nothing to fear," he added as he saw the white and frightened face of the young girl. "I've been talking to him. He's agreed to show us the way to the gates of the city of the giants. Come along and meet him."

He led them outside. There stood two black boots.

63

And up and up into the mist grew the figure of the giant. His face was just a gray blur to the gods who stood like dwarfs below him.

"These are my friends," Thor shouted to the giant. "Lead on and we will follow." The giant bent down to pick up his mitten and grinned at them. His mouth looked like a great cavern with a row of white stones. His breath was hot in their faces. Then he started out into the mist. The gods and their servants followed the black heels of his huge boots. They were nearing the end of their journey.

CHAPTER VIII

The Contest with the Giants

For another whole day Thor and Loki and the two peasants followed the giant through the land of mist. When night came, the giant lay down upon the ground. He tossed his knapsack over to Thor and told him and his companions to eat all they wanted of the food that was in it. Then he went to sleep.

Thor and Loki pulled and tugged at the straps that tied the sack together. Thialfi and his sister tried to help. All four pulled and pulled. With sticks and stones they tried to pry the knots apart. Then they tried to cut the thick leather, but nothing would rip the tough hide. Finally they gave up and went to bed hungry.

But even sleep was impossible, for this night the giant's snores were worse than before. The earth trembled constantly while his deep breathing roared in their ears. Thor was terribly angry at such rudeness. He was sure the giant knew they would not be able to open the knapsack of food. And now he kept them awake with his snores. Thor, the thunder god, would teach him a lesson! And he took his great hammer from his belt, and struck the giant on the forehead. The giant stirred slightly and turned over.

"Was that a leaf that fell upon my head?" he murmured, and began to snore again. The peasants and gods looked at each other in wonder. Could it be that the blow had not even hurt this great creature? Thor ran his hand through his red hair and scowled up at the huge body of the sleeping giant. Once again he raised his hammer and hurled it with all his might at the giant. Again the giant stirred in his sleep.

"A piece of bark must have fallen on my face," he complained.

"Try again!" cried Loki. "Draw in your belt so you can put more strength behind it. Something must have gone wrong before. Perhaps you didn't hit him squarely."

So again Thor threw his hammer at the giant. This time the huge man sat up. "Umph!" he grumbled. "It's late in the night for birds to be dropping twigs from the trees. But I'm sure one just fell on my head. Well, there's still time to get some more sleep." And he rolled onto his side with a great yawn.

Thor shook his fist at the giant's back, and tried not to show the young peasants how upset he was. Loki shook his head, and leaned against a tree, trying to rest in spite of everything. They would need all their strength and more the next morning, if Thor's hammer could not defend them against the giants.

When the next morning finally came, the giant pointed to a road which he said would lead them straight to the palace of the king of the giants. Then he left them. Down the road went the two gods and the two peasants. Suddenly out of the heavy mist in front of them arose a silvery castle. It was made of great gleaming blocks of ice. The beautiful glittering pillars were icicles, and the roofs of the high towers and halls were of the whitest snow. A cold blast of icy wind whipped around the corners and blew down the road into the faces of the travelers, making their eyes water and their noses sting.

Across the entrance to this magnificent castle was a gate of heavy bars. But the gods were small enough to slip through the spaces between the bars, and thus they entered the castle and stood before the king of the giants. The king was sitting on a throne at the end of a tremendous hall. Other great giants stood around laughing and talking till they saw the strangers enter. Then a dead silence fell on the court.

The king peered down at the little gods and their servants. He stretched his great thick neck to see them over his huge knees, and he leaned forward on his throne of rocks and ice in order to hear what they said. For although Thor and Loki shouted, their voices had to carry a long way before they reached the giant king's ears.

"So you are the great gods I have heard so much about," bellowed the king. "How small you are!" And his laugh rang from the high rafters. It echoed a hundred times throughout the palace hall. "How small! How small! How small!" came from every corner.

"Surely creatures as small as you cannot do all that we are told you do!" All the other giants stood looking at them and grinning.

At this Loki stepped closer to the king. No one was going to make fun of him!

"We may not be as large as you, but we are far wiser and cleverer. We can do all that you can do — and better than you can do it!"

"What's that?" said the giant. "Speak up. I can't

hear you." And the king leaned even further forward on his throne.

"He must be deaf," muttered Thor angrily. He stepped up beside Loki and repeated what the other god had said in his voice of thunder. But the thunder in the land of the giants seemed like a far distant grumbling. It wasn't even loud enough to echo from the rafters.

"He must have a cold," the king said to one of his attendants. Then he leaned back on his throne and waved his hand at everyone in the hall. "Well, let us have a contest to prove whether what these gods say is true. What do you wish to do?" he shouted down to Loki. Loki's face still burned red with anger. But his stomach was empty and ached from a day without food. He said he could eat more than any giant right then, and twice as fast.

"Very well," said the king. And he ordered his cook to match his hunger with Loki's. A long, narrow wooden dish was placed on the floor. It was so long it stretched across the width of the giants' hall. It was full of a hot meat stew. Loki sat at one end of the wooden dish, and the giant cook at the other. The delicious smell of the food made the hungry Loki grin and forget the jeering giants. When the king gave the signal, the cook and Loki began to gulp down the food.

Finally Loki reached the center of the long dish and looked up in triumph. But, alas, there sat the cook beside him! And the cook had eaten all the bones and his half of the wooden dish!

The giants roared with laughter as they saw the look of surprise and anger on Loki's face. Loki sprang to his feet and went over to Thor.

"There's some strange magic in this," he whispered. "We gods are not so weak. Why, if these giants are so strong, do they fear us when we are in Asgard?"

"I do not understand," said Thor with a dark scowl.

"Well," chuckled the king, "perhaps you can do better at something else."

"My thirst is never satisfied," cried Thor, stepping forward. "In one breath I can drain the largest drinking vessel you have in the palace."

At once a large horn was brought into the hall and handed to Thor. It was filled to the brim with rich brown ale. Thor took it in his strong hands. He threw back his head and drew a deep breath. Then he lifted the great horn to his lips and drank and drank. Great blue veins stood out on his forehead and his face grew redder and redder until it turned purple. And still he drank. Loki and the peasants looked on with pride. But the giants only smiled.

At last, with a gasp, Thor lowered the horn from his lips. Everyone crowded forward to look into the horn. Lo, the ale had only gone down an inch! It could not be. Thor looked again, but the ale was only a little way from the top.

"Try again," urged the king. "Really good drinkers here can empty it the first time. Moderately thirsty ones take two gulps, whereas small drinkers take all of three." So Thor tried again. And again he had barely lowered the line of the ale in the great horn. A third time he did no better. Finally he sat down, defeated.

Then up jumped the peasant boy, Thialfi. He challenged any one of the giants in a race. A young giant stood up and they went forth to a great bare field around which they ran like the wind. Thor and Loki were surprised to see Thialfi's grace and speed, but the giant soon overtook him. Once more the gods lost the contest.

But Thor refused to give up. With his hand on his magic belt, he suggested a wrestling match.

"Come," said the giant, "I admire your courage, but look at your size. It is a foolish challenge."

"Do you refuse?" cried Thor angrily.

"Well, no. But I can hardly let anyone stronger than my old nurse here wrestle with you. I shouldn't like to see any real harm come to one of the great gods while on a friendly visit in the land of the giants."

There was nothing for Thor to do but go ahead and wrestle with an old woman. His hair flamed even brighter and his scowl darkened his face. Such insults were too much to bear! Even so, he tightened his belt and rolled up his sleeves and took his stand. Then the old woman and the great thunder god rolled and struggled, turned and tussled on the floor in the center of the hall until at last Thor was thrown. He had lost the match.

When Thor — still determined to do something successfully — suggested proving his strength by weight lifting, the giants' cat was brought into the room. Indeed it was such a big cat, it looked like a tiger. However, Thor tightened his belt once again with satisfaction. He knew he had lifted far heavier weights than this cat. He bent with a smile over the cat's back and put his arms around its body. Then he heaved with all his might, expecting to toss it to the high rafters. It did not budge! He tugged and pushed and pulled, but the cat did not move!

"There's some strange magic in this," he could hear Loki mutter. And Thor agreed, but he was determined to try once more. Taking a deep breath, he gritted his teeth and with a tremendous jerk managed to lift one of the cat's paws from the ground.

Roars of laughter from the giants was Thor's reward.

"Well, well," said the king. "Better luck next time. But after this, perhaps you gods will speak with more respect of us giants. In the morning I will take you to the edge of our land and see you started on your way back to Asgard."

There was nothing left for the gods and peasants to do but rest and prepare for the morning's journey.

The next morning the king of the giants looked at them with a new light in his eyes. As they stood in the cold gray mist at the edge of the sea he said, "Thor and Loki, now that you are leaving my kingdom, I have something to tell you. If I had ever guessed what strength and courage you had, I never would have let you enter my palace. For I was the giant whose snores woke you. I was the giant who led you to my own gates."

The giant turned to the red-haired god. "When you, Thor," he continued, "struck at me with your hammer, you hit a mountain instead of my forehead. I feared your hammer. By my magic I placed an invisible mountain between you and me. If you could see the great cracks your hammer made in that mountain, you would know why I fear you."

Then the giant turned to Loki, who stood looking at him with raised eyebrows. "My cook, who ate more and faster than you, was really *wild fire,* which destroys all. And your servant, Thialfi, ran a race with *thought,* which travels more swiftly than any runner.

"That horn from which you drank, Thor, my friend, was connected with the sea, which nobody can empty. And my nurse was *old age,* whom none can resist. The cat was in fact the terrible snake which twists itself around the world. When you managed to lift one of its feet, we were terrified for fear you would actually loosen the horrible creature and bring destruction to us all. So you see why I will never again allow such as you to enter the land of the giants. Only by our knowledge of magic can we defeat the gods!"

At this, Thor roared with rage. So Loki had been right! It had not been a fair contest. And he raised his hammer in anger. But the mist had grown thicker and grayer, and the giant king had disappeared.

"You see!" said Loki with a satisfied smile. But Thor said nothing, for he was staring down at the shore of the sea. Several feet above the place where the waves now washed the sand a dark line marked where the water had been. Thor smiled. He knew now that he had drunk long and well from the great horn. Certainly he had done better than any other god could have done, and far better than any giant. He was content at last to return to Asgard where the bright sun shone.

CHAPTER IX

Idun and the Golden Apples

IDUN was one of the best-loved goddesses in Asgard. She was young and fresh as a flower of spring. One day she had come smiling into Asgard with a basket over her arm. As the gods and goddesses crowded around to welcome this lovely young woman, Idun showed them what was in her basket. When she lifted the cover, the sun flashed on something very bright. Dazzled at first by the brilliance, they came to realize that Idun's basket was full of golden apples. To their surprise and delight, she gave one to each and every god and goddess.

"Eat these," said Idun, "and you will never grow old. You will never have gray hair. You will never grow lame and tired in body and heart. As long as I am in Asgard, I will give you these apples to eat."

The gods shouted Idun's praises. The goddesses sang to her and showered her with spring blossoms.

All rejoiced that Idun and her golden apples had come to Asgard.

One day, not long afterwards, Loki and two friends crossed the rainbow bridge for another of their adventures on earth. By noon they were tired and very hungry. Seeing a herd of oxen Loki killed one and prepared it for roasting. The other gods built a roaring fire, and then they all sat around it waiting for the meat to cook.

But no tempting odor floated on the air. No rich meaty juices dripped into the fire. The meat remained as raw as though it had never been near a flame. The gods threw more wood on the fire until it grew so hot they had to move away from it. Still the meat remained raw. They could not understand the power that kept it so, and knew there must be strange magic in it.

Presently they noticed a huge eagle sitting on the limb of a nearby tree. The bird began to speak. "You must be very hungry," and his large, sharp beak snapped out the words. "I can help," he said, winking one of his beady eyes. "But you must let me have as much of that ox as I can eat."

"Very well," the gods agreed, for they were so hungry by this time that they would promise anything in order to eat. Besides, they thought there was enough for all.

So the great bird swooped down from his perch and fanned the flames with his huge wings. Now the fire roared, and the most delicious odor of roasting meat drifted in the air. The gods licked their lips and thought how good it would taste. But when the eagle started to carry off three quarters of the ox, they called out angrily. Indeed that was more than his share!

Loki began to beat the eagle with a stick. "You can't eat all that!" he cried as he struck again and again. But suddenly Loki gasped with horror. The stick had become fastened to the great eagle, and Loki's hands were fast to the stick! Screaming with triumph, the eagle sailed up and up into the sky, Loki dangling behind. Poor Loki's arms were nearly pulled out of his body.

"Put me down! Put me down!" he cried. The eagle paid no attention. "You can have all the ox, if you'll just put me down!" But the eagle clamped his beak tighter together and flew on.

"Please! Please!" begged Loki. His whole body ached and his arms felt as though they would break off. "What do you wish? I'll do anything you say! Just put me down!"

Then the eagle spoke.

"I am the storm giant Thiassi. If you will promise upon the most solemn oaths to bring the lovely Idun out of Asgard so that I may capture her and eat her magic fruit, I will set you free."

"That is too much!" cried Loki, thinking with fear of what would happen if he betrayed the beloved Idun. "Anything but that!"

"That is the only way to save yourself. I want Idun and her golden apples!" With this the great eagle swooped and circled, swinging poor Loki till he screamed with pain.

"Stop! I will do it," he gasped. "Somehow I'll get Idun out of Asgard!"

Tired and sore, Loki limped back to the city of the gods. The other gods greeted him kindly, and he was careful not to tell them about the bargain he had made with the giant.

The very next day Loki went to look for Idun in her orchard. There he found her singing to herself as she wandered under the blossoming trees. "Fair Idun," Loki called to her, "you will never guess what I saw outside the gates of Asgard."

"What was it?" smiled Idun. "Tell me."

"Golden apples just like yours. Whole trees with their branches bending low under the weight of the golden fruit."

"Oh, no!" cried Idun in surprise. "I am sure you must be mistaken. The apples cannot be exactly like mine, for I am the only one who has the golden apples of youth."

"Come and see for yourself, then," said Loki slyly. Idun took a beautiful crystal bowl and filled it with her apples. Then she followed Loki out of the gates of Asgard to compare her fruit with the apples which he said he had found.

Once out of sight of Asgard wicked Loki disappeared. When Idun found herself standing alone in a strange field, she called out, "Loki! Loki! Where have you gone?"

There was no answer. She heard only the peep of a bird and the rustle of an animal in the long grass. Then, with a great sound of flapping wings the huge eagle blackened the sky. Down and down he flew, straight toward lovely Idun. Snatching her up, he bore her with her golden apples away to his palace.

There was no one to hear Idun's sad cries for help. No one for her to turn to in the land of the giants. Day after day she sat in the cold and darkness of Thiassi's palace. No sound of happy voices broke the stillness. When Thiassi spoke to her, the echo of his voice growled among the stone pillars, but brave Idun held tight to her crystal bowl. She refused to give Thiassi even one bite of a golden apple.

Meanwhile the gods and goddesses began to wonder where Idun had gone. At first they were not alarmed. They knew how Idun loved to wander through fields and orchards talking to the birds and animals. They thought she was with friends. But as the days passed and she did not appear they became worried. Before long they must have more of her apples.

Days passed, and Idun was nowhere to be seen. Some of the gods complained of aches and pains in their legs. Frigga gasped with horror when she saw herself in the mirror. Her hair was turning white! And powerful Thor saw his hand beginning to tremble — that hand that held the great hammer! Even Odin felt weary at the end of a day. Idun must be found! The gods and goddesses needed to eat again from her basket of apples.

The rumor grew in Asgard that Loki was the last to have been seen with Idun. And before long the young god was forced to admit what he had done.

"You are a fool!" Odin said to Loki. "You have done a wicked thing, and as always in so doing you have harmed yourself. What are we in Asgard to do without our lovely Idun and her golden fruit? We will grow old and feeble, while the giants stay young and strong. It is up to you to rescue Idun. You must free her from the giant."

"But . . ." began Loki. He had a hundred excuses on the tip of his tongue.

"You must find Idun and bring her and her apples back to Asgard," Odin said again. Time was too short to listen to Loki's protests. "Hurry!" the great king ordered angrily.

So Loki ran swiftly to the palace of Freya, the goddess of love and beauty. She was the most beautiful woman in Asgard. Her hair was like the golden rays of the sun, her eyes were as blue as violets, and her bright jewels almost blinded the men who gazed upon her. She owned many treasures, among them a pair of wings made of silver-gray feathers, with which she could fly through the air as easily as any bird.

Loki wanted to borrow those wings. When he told Freya about the dreadful thing he had done, when he told her he was going to try to rescue Idun, she was glad to lend them to him. How dreadful if she, the goddess of beauty, should grow wrinkled and old!

"Hurry! Hurry!" Freya called after Loki. "Don't you dare return without dear Idun and her apples!"

Quickly fastening the wings to his shoulders, Loki flew to the land of the giants. When he came to Thiassi's palace he sat down on a boulder near the gates and pulled the silvery wings around him. He looked like a bird enjoying a nap with his head tucked in his feathers. Soon Thiassi came out, prepared to go fishing. Loki watched him stride along the road to the ocean until he was out of sight. Then he rushed into the palace to find Idun.

There sat the poor Idun, shivering with cold and fear, but still clutching the crystal bowl of golden apples. Loki hurried her out of the gates. Then by means of his magic he turned her into a smooth brown nut and, holding the nut tightly, flew as fast as he could back to Asgard.

The gods and goddesses stood at the city gates watching for Loki's return. Would he bring Idun and her apples safely back to them? Perhaps Idun had already been forced to give up her apples. Perhaps Loki would be captured by the giants. They all looked anxiously at the far horizon.

"See there!" shouted Thor. "That speck. Could it be . . . ?"

"Oh yes! I see it!" cried one of the goddesses. And indeed there was a tiny speck that grew larger and larger as it flew closer. Soon they saw it was Loki holding something in his hands.

"But look!" another god shouted. "Someone is chasing him!" And they watched the huge eagle following close behind.

"He's gaining on him!" one of the goddesses cried.

"Hurry," commanded Odin. "Lay kindling and branches and logs around the walls of the city." And all the gods and their helpers rushed to obey.

"Oh," groaned Frigga, wringing her hands. "The eagle flies so swiftly! Loki, go faster! Faster!" she screamed.

Poor Loki beat the air with his wings. Only a few more feet to safety. He could hear the swish of the eagle's wings. He could even hear the eagle's harsh breathing. Then he fell exhausted at Odin's feet, but even as he did so he turned Idun back into her lovely self.

Quickly the gods lit the fires they had laid. The flames leaped up and up, burning the wings of the wicked eagle. With a shriek the great bird fell into the fire. So Thiassi, the storm giant, was killed. And the gods and goddesses helped themselves happily to Idun's golden fruit.

CHAPTER X

The Flea and the Necklace

MANY of the gods were clever and wise. But next to the great Odin, Heimdall was the wisest of all in Asgard. Heimdall was the one who guarded the rainbow bridge. He was always dressed in white armor. At night his tall figure would rise gleaming out of the soft darkness that covered Asgard. A flashing sword hung at his waist. Around his neck was his marvelous curved trumpet, ready to blow whenever he saw an enemy drawing near. Its sound would echo from every corner of the world and waken every living creature.

Heimdall watched and listened from the highest point on the bridge that curved from the roots of the great ever green tree to the city of the gods. His eyes were so keen that he could see plainly everything for a hundred miles — by night as well as by day. His ears were so sharp that he could hear the grass grow on the hillside. He could hear the wool grow on a sheep's back. And he needed less sleep than a bird. Who could be as perfect a watchman?

One night Heimdall was startled by soft footsteps creeping catlike in the direction of the palace of Freya, goddess of beauty. Who could be about so late? No one, surely, who was up to any good. Heimdall turned his eagle gaze upon Freya's dwelling. A shadow was moving across the gardens. In spite of the darkness, he saw that it was the young troublemaker, Loki. Even as he watched, Loki turned himself into a fly and buzzed through Freya's bedroom window.

Inside the palace Loki stood in his real form again, looking down at the sleeping Freya. She was very beautiful as she lay peacefully in bed. Her golden head was pillowed on her white arm. Her hair fell softly about her shoulders, spring flowers still clinging to the thick waves.

But Loki did not gaze long at the goddess. It was the glittering necklace clasped about her pale throat which interested him most. It was Freya's most beloved possession. It twinkled and sparkled as though made of the most glorious stars in the sky. Each stone seemed to have a glowing fire in its heart.

Loki remembered this wonderful necklace well.

Those burning jewels had taken his eye when he begged Freya to lend him her wings. Ever since he had longed to own that necklace. Nowhere in all the world was there another of such beauty and value. Not even Frigga's gold necklace had been as fine. But Freya lay upon the clasp. To move her would waken her, and all would be lost.

Unaware of Heimdall's watching eyes, Loki turned himself into a flea and crept between the sleeping Freya and her bed. He stung her on her side — a sting ever so gentle, not enough to waken her. She turned in annoyance. The clasp of the necklace was now easy to reach. Quickly Loki unfastened it and slipped the jewels from the goddess's throat. Then, changing back to a fly, Loki flew out of the window with the necklace.

Just as quickly Heimdall sprang to catch the midnight thief. Racing across the bridge he leaped over the palace wall — flashing like a comet through the night. In no time he was upon Loki, drawing his sword to cut off that mischievous head. But Loki was not so easily caught. Heimdall found himself slashing out at a flickering blue flame! Another of Loki's quick changes had saved his head.

However, Heimdall was his match. He changed

himself into a cloud and poured down a torrent of rain to put out the flame. The flame began to sputter, but the sputter turned to a growl. And there was a great white polar bear, with open jaws ready to swallow the water.

Heimdall, more than ready for a fight, also turned himself into a bear. The two bears growled and snapped at each other, struck out with sharp-clawed paws, rolled in a grim struggle. When Heimdall's teeth started to sink into Loki's neck, the fire god turned himself into a seal. Heimdall became a seal, too, with strong yellow teeth. So the struggle continued.

The animals of the night drew near to watch this battle between two powerful gods. They crouched breathless and still, frozen with awe. The owls hunched in their feathers, their round yellow eyes unblinking. Gray wolves hovered like ghosts in the darkness. The bats swooped silently, closer and closer. Far away, the giants and dwarfs felt the earth shake, but they did not know about the terrible fight between two gods who had turned themselves into beasts.

At last Loki saw that he was going to be beaten, no matter what he did. But he did not want to die. Life was full of too many good things. It would be better to turn himself back to his real form and give up the necklace. So, with bowed head, he handed over the glittering jewels to the wise god in white armor.

Heimdall returned the necklace to Freya before she had discovered that it was missing.

When the other gods heard the story, they shook their heads sadly. What was to be done about Loki? To play harmless pranks — that was one thing. But to steal . . . It was well they had so keen a watchman to guard their city against evil — even the evil among themselves.

CHAPTER XI

Balder the Beautiful

ODIN and Frigga had twin sons named Balder and Hodur. Unlike most twins, they were as different as day and night.

Hodur was dark and serious. He was very quiet and seemed always to be thinking unhappy thoughts. That was not strange, for Hodur was blind. He had never seen the sunshine. He had never seen his father and mother. He had never seen the beautiful city of the gods where he lived.

Hodur could learn things only by feeling and listening in the darkness. He had to believe what he was told. He could hear the other gods laugh and play, but he could not take part in their games!

Hodur's twin brother Balder was like the sunshine itself. He was tall and fair — the handsomest god in Asgard. And he was the favorite of all, for no one laughed so merrily, no one was quite so kind and loving, no one cheered and warmed the hearts of men and women like this young god of light.

Balder lived with his beautiful young wife Nanna in a great palace with a silver roof and golden pillars. The gods and goddesses were always welcome in his home and they went there often to enjoy the gaiety and happiness they found there.

But one day Odin and Frigga were surprised to see a sadness in their son's face. He greeted them as usual with his happy smile. He laughed and joked. But there was a new stillness, a puzzled, unhappy look, in the depths of his eyes.

"Something is troubling you, dear son," cried Frigga. "Tell me what it is. Perhaps I can help you." Balder laughed and said she was imagining things.

"No, son. I see what your mother sees," said Odin. "Can't we help?" A slight frown appeared then on Balder's smooth white forehead. He put up his hand as if to rub it out.

"I do not know how to tell you," he said slowly. Balder's father and mother were startled at the serious tone in his voice. "Lately I have had strange dreams . . . unhappy dreams that seem to be signs of some terrible trouble. In the morning I cannot remember them. I only remember the cold touch of fear they leave on my heart."

"You are overtired, my son," comforted Frigga. "When you are rested these dreams will go."

"You think too much of others' troubles. Your mother is right," agreed Odin. "Do not trouble yourself about mere dreams. Everyone loves you. Nothing would harm you. You are the favorite of all!"

But when Odin and Frigga were alone in their own palace, they both admitted they were worried. The gods believed that dreams were sent to warn people of danger. How terrible if anything should happen to their dear son!

"I suppose someone might harm Balder without meaning to," said Frigga. "I will have my messengers go to all parts of the world and tell every living creature, every plant, and all the metals and stones to take a solemn vow that they will do no harm to Balder." And she hurried off to give her orders.

Frigga's plan was a good one, but Odin was not satisfied. When the All-father had drunk from Mimir's well, one of his eyes had bought him the knowledge of the future. He knew that Balder was doomed to die. But surely not so soon! He decided to go himself to the land of the dead and there persuade the prophetess Vala to rise from her grave. She alone could tell him more than he already knew of what was going to be. It was a long, long voyage with many dangers, but Odin felt he must be prepared for the future, whatever it might be.

Soon after Odin left, Frigga s messengers began to return, one by one. She welcomed them as she sat spinning her golden thread. Each one told her of the far corner of the world that she had visited. Each told of how glad even the sticks and stones were to give their promise never to hurt Balder. Everyone had promised, down to the smallest fly and the tiniest pebble on the beach.

"All things love Balder!" cried the messengers. And Frigga smiled and sighed with relief. Now, surely, no harm would come to her beloved son. She went on spinning, singing softly to herself. All was well in the city of the gods.

Meanwhile Odin dashed across the shimmering rainbow bridge. Swiftly the great eight-legged horse carried the All-father down and down the steep way to the land of the dead. Past the gate of Hel's kingdom they raced, past the growling watchdog. When at last Odin came into Hel's damp and gloomy palace he found huge torches burning to light the dark rooms. A great feast was being prepared. The couches were covered with rich tapestries as though some greatly honored guest were expected.

Odin hurried on, afraid to think for whom they might be waiting. Finally he came to the grave of the prophetess Vala. There it was, gray and still under a little cloud of cold mist. There it had been for many a year, undisturbed by any voice from the living.

Looking down upon the grave, the great Odin muttered magic words. Three times he repeated the spell that would raise the dead. Then with a soft rustling noise, like the wind whispering in dry leaves, the grave opened. A misty figure wrapped in a white cloth rose slowly, wringing her hands. The whispering became a hollow voice that breathed with the wind.

"What do you of the living wish of me? What would you have of one so long dead?" asked the voice. And Odin asked who was going to be honored at the great feast that Hel was preparing.

"Balder the beautiful, the god of purity and light, is expected here. He will be killed by his blind brother. Hodur will do the terrible deed and Odin's son will be no more in Asgard." And the prophetess started to fade back into the dark pit of her grave.

"No! No!" the great king cried, covering his face

with his hands. It was worse than he had feared. But Odin knew that nothing could change the word of the future. One question more must be asked before the prophetess returned to her silence.

"Who will bring punishment down upon the murderer? Who will avenge Balder's death?"

"Another son of Odin," whispered the hollow voice. "A son not yet born. He will avenge Balder's death. He will neither wash his face nor comb his hair until he sees justice done!"

What a strange answer! What could it mean? All was still. The prophetess had returned to her grave, to be silent forever more. Slowly and sadly Odin went back to his gray horse and rode his weary way up to Asgard.

When Odin reached the golden city of the gods, all seemed well, however. The sun felt warm and soothing after the cold dampness of Hel's land. Frigga was spinning and singing. The grass was green. Balder was laughing and joking with his friends. Perhaps the terrible future foretold by the prophetess was far off. Certainly Balder was safe if all things had vowed never to harm him. Odin tried to forget what he had learned in the land of the dead.

CHAPTER XII

The Mark of the Mistletoe

WHEN Frigga told everyone in Asgard that all things had promised never to harm Balder, the great city rang with rejoicing. The young gods gathered on the green plain to play games. They soon tired of the old contest of throwing disks, however, and tried to think of a new game.

Later no one could remember who had thought of the new game first, but Balder had been as eager to play it as any of them. Since nothing could hurt the god of light, why not use him as a target? Balder stood alone some distance from the others while they aimed all kinds of weapons at him.

At first some of the gods were afraid, but when they saw a huge rock hurled straight at Balder bounce unnoticed from his shoulder, when a spear flying straight toward his heart fell harmless at his feet, and when an arrow swerved of its own will to avoid hitting the son of Odin, they, too, joined in the delight of the others.

Everyone tried to think of a new weapon. And, again and again, as each one failed even to scratch Balder, they cheered and laughed.

Now Loki stood by watching all this. Ever since he had stolen Freya's necklace, the gods had frowned upon him. They no longer laughed at his pranks and funny stories. They no longer invited him to join them. He was without a friend. And the handsome god of light was the favorite of all.

How silly everyone was to make such a fuss over Balder! Of course he was handsome and pleasant, but he was not very clever, thought Loki. The fire god was jealous and angry at the way he had been treated because he had done one thing wrong. He forgot how many times he had displeased the gods.

As he watched the others enjoying the new sport, his heart grew hot with rage. He'd show these happy young fools! And he changed himself into an old woman and hobbled slowly past Frigga's palace.

The queen of the gods sat spinning quietly in the warm sunshine. She smiled to herself when the gay laughter drifted on the breeze from the plain. There were cheers and shouts and more laughter. She wondered what it was all about and, looking up, saw the old woman passing by.

"What makes my son and his friends so merry, my good woman?" Frigga called out. The old woman stopped and smiled a toothless smile. In a quavering voice she told the goddess about the new game they had invented with Balder for a target. Frigga gasped in surprise, but then smiled confidently.

"Are you not afraid that something will be found to hurt him?" asked the old woman.

"Oh no," replied Frigga. "At first I was worried, but then I remembered that all things have promised never to hurt my dearest son. The world knows that it could not bear to be without him."

"*All* things gave their promise?" cried the old woman in wonder. "Do you mean that every little thing in this great world took that vow?"

"Yes," said Frigga, "my messengers went to every living thing, every rock and stone — that is, except the mistletoe. The little plant that grows on the old oak at the gates of Asgard is so weak and small that it could do no harm. My messengers didn't bother the poor thing. No, I am not worried."

"I hope you will never have reason to think you have been foolish," said the old woman and went away.

It was Loki who went to the gates of Asgard and found the mistletoe with its waxy white berries growing where Frigga had said. He cut off a piece and with his magic power made its weak stem grow thick and hard. Then with his knife he carved it into a strange-looking arrowhead. It was a very sharp arrowhead. He let it prick the palm of his hand and smiled with satisfaction. Then he joined the other gods on the plain where they were still throwing things at Balder.

Balder's brother Hodur stood silently at the side leaning against a tree trunk. As he stared with his blind eyes in the direction of the laughter he looked lonely and unhappy. Loki went softly over to him.

"Well, Hodur," he said. The poor blind man jumped at the sound of a voice so near.

"Who is it?" he asked.

"Loki, your friend Loki. Why are you not taking part in this sport? Have you nothing to throw at your brother?"

"Do not tease me," begged the god of darkness. "You know well enough that I cannot see. How could I take part in the fun?"

"Come! Come!" laughed Loki. "Do not be so serious. I meant no harm. I was going to suggest that you let me help you. I have a little twig here. Let me fasten it to a pole and guide your arm. Then you, too, can honor your brother in this silly game."

"I would look so foolish," Hodur objected.

"Nobody will notice. They're too busy throwing their own weapons. Come on!" And Loki shoved Hodur forward. He attached the arrowhead of mistletoe to the end of a stick and placed it in Hodur's hand. Then, guiding the blind god's elbow, he sent it swiftly to its mark.

There was a cry from Balder, and a heavy thud. Sudden silence fell upon the plain. Then horrified cries came from the gods.

"What has happened?" gasped Hodur. "What does it mean?" But Loki had slipped silently away and Hodur stood alone.

"Balder! Balder!" called the voices. And then — "He's dead! Someone has slain our beautiful Balder!"

"Look! Look!" cried one voice above the others. "Look at Hodur!" Hodur stood just where he had been when Loki guided his arm. He could feel the gods turn and stare at him. What could he have thrown at his brother? Could he . . . ? Oh no! But the angry frightened voices drew closer until they seemed to be pressing around him. Then Hodur knew. Somehow, by Loki's trick he had killed his own brother! He covered his face with his hands and stumbled across the plain — away from the moaning crowd.

CHAPTER XIII

The One
Who Would Not Weep

THE GODS stared at Balder lying among the swords and spears that had failed to hurt him. They could not believe their eyes. What had happened? What magic thing had pierced his heart in spite of all the promises sent to Frigga?

And there was blind Hodur, alone in the middle of the plain. Terrible pain and guilt were written on his sad face. What had he thrown at his shining brother? As he turned to leave, the gods rushed after him with angry cries. He must pay for this dreadful crime! But Odin's voice stopped them. It rang sternly across the field.

"Stop! No violence will be done in the city of the gods. Let my poor blind son go! It is no fault of his. Our tragedy was planned by the Fates. This I learned in Hel's land: Balder will be avenged, but by none of you." A great sigh, like a cold, cheerless wind, drifted over Asgard at these words. All the gods had sighed together.

"Come!" cried Odin. "Let us pay our last farewell to our beloved Balder." And the great king led them back to the body of the god of light.

Already Frigga and Balder's young wife, Nanna, were kneeling by his side. They wept and pleaded with him to speak. But Balder lay still and silent. When poor Nanna saw this she understood that nothing could help. With a cry she threw herself upon her husband and died of a broken heart. Now she could go with him on the long, cold journey to Hel's land. Now she would never be parted from him.

This was as it should be. The gods knew that. And sadly they began to prepare for a funeral at which all honors would be given to this great son of Odin. But Frigga wept and wrung her hands.

"Can nothing be done? Must such wickedness be borne? Surely someone can plead with Hel to send our Balder back to us! Surely she will listen to reason! The world cannot go on without the light and goodness of Balder."

Odin put his arm around Frigga and led her toward

their palace. He shook his head sadly. "It is the way the prophetess Vala foretold it. I myself saw the banquet laid in Hel's hall for our dear son. It is useless to fight the Fates."

"You always say that," cried Frigga angrily. "But we can try. We might be able to bargain with Hel."

So it was that Hermod, swift messenger of the gods, put on his gleaming helmet and, with his magic staff under his arm, set out for the land of the dead. He dashed through the gates of Asgard on the back of the great eight-footed steed that Odin loaned him. The gods, with tears in their eyes, waved him off.

While Hermod traveled on his cheerless way, all Asgard busied itself preparing a great funeral for Balder. The gods believed that the body was honored by being burned in the glory of flames. Then it would live again in the land of the dead. All Balder's favorite possessions were laid beside him and his wife on a great ship. Even his horse and hounds, his shield and weapons, were placed carefully within his reach. Then each god brought his own most prized possession to the ship, in this way showing his love for Balder.

Some brought their swords. Others laid a treasured jewel or a favorite gauntlet near his hand. And last of all the great Odin stepped forward. While the black ravens flew round his head, he placed the magic ring that Sindri had made upon his son's breast. Then he bent close to Balder's ear and whispered his words of farewell.

At last the ship was ready to be pushed into the sea. But it was so laden with treasure that no god — not even Thor, the thunder god — was able to move it. Finally a giantess was persuaded to come and lend her strength, and the great ship shot into the waves. All the earth shook as if from an earthquake. Then Thor set fire to the ship with his magic hammer and the gods stood on the shore in grief-stricken silence, watching it burn.

The flames leaped up and up in a glory of crimson as the ship drifted out into the dark waters. Further and further away it floated until it was a brilliant glow on the horizon like the setting sun. And truly the sun was setting for those in Asgard, without Balder.

"Say he will come back to us!" sobbed Frigga. But Odin only shook his head.

Meanwhile, for nine days and nights, Hermod traveled the rough and dangerous way down to Hel.

At last he reached Hel's gate, only to find it closed and barred. So he jumped off Odin's steed and stood on the ice that paved the way. Carefully he tightened the saddle. Then, remounting and spurring the great gray horse, he leaped with ease over the high gate. On he rushed to Hel's banquet hall. There he found Balder and Nanna, already arrived in this dark and dreary land. Balder smiled and shook his head sadly when Hermod told him the reason for his errand.

"It will do no good, dear friend," said Balder. "Hel will not listen to you. Her heart is of ice. Beware of her bargains. She is not to be trusted."

But Hermod sought out the lady of death. Carefully he put his request to her. Did she know that the earth could never be happy without Balder? Had she no pity in her heart for Odin and Frigga? Hel listened in brooding silence. At last she spoke, and her voice echoed in hollow notes throughout the land that held the dead.

"If it is as you say," she said, "if all love Balder so dearly, let all things weep. If every god, man and beast, if all plants and sticks and stones will weep for Balder's death, then I will send him back to Asgard. But let one

refuse to shed a tear and here your god of sunshine will remain."

Swiftly Hermod leaped to his feet with thanks upon his lips. He was sure that all things would gladly weep for Balder! He raced back to Asgard rejoicing in his heart. But he had not seen Hel's grim smile. Hel knew there was one who would not weep.

Hope lived again in the hearts of the gods when they crowded around the triumphant Hermod. Of course all would gladly weep! Their tears would moisten the earth like the spring thaws. Balder's return would warm the land and bring forth the bright flowers and green grass. All would be well again. Only Odin shook his head.

The messengers rushed out over the world, bidding all to weep. The wind whispered to the leaves in the trees and to the grass and flowers on the hillsides. The streams gurgled the message through the land. The birds sang the tidings to the animals. And all gladly wept.

But as the messengers were returning, sure that the word had reached all, they passed a dark cave. At the mouth of the cave crouched an ugly giantess. The messengers stopped and told her their news.

"So shed your tear for Balder, and the sun will shine upon you!" they cried. But the giantess turned and fled into the blackness of the cave.

"Never a tear will I shed for your dear Balder. Hel may keep that god and all his glory!" And the giantess laughed. It was an ugly sound that rang from the hollows in the rocks. It had also a familiar sound. The messengers knew it was Loki's laugh.

So it was that jealous Loki became wholly evil and prevented Balder from returning to Asgard. The gods knew that a world which held such wickedness was doomed. The great battle must be near at hand. With heavy hearts they returned to their palaces.

CHAPTER XIV

The Twilight of the Gods

THE EVIL in Loki had grown so great that he no longer cared about the good things in Asgard. He hated all the gods. He was glad that Balder would never come back. He was proud of the way he had tricked poor blind Hodur into killing his beloved brother. Not for one minute was he sorry that he had pretended to be a giantess and refused to shed a tear for Balder.

The gods knew all this. It made them sad and afraid. They had forgiven Loki for too many things too many times. They had allowed his evil to live with them and it had brought this great sadness upon them. Odin knew it was too late to save Asgard, but he agreed that Loki must be banished to the earth. He must never again be allowed to enter the city of the gods.

But Loki only laughed.

"Don't worry," he said scornfully. "I have no wish

to stay in Asgard. It is a dull place full of stupid people. Besides, the end is near. I will make you pay for your insults!" And the fire god stalked across the rainbow bridge with his head in the air.

Now the gods were very angry. And when they saw Loki spreading wicked thoughts among the men and women of the earth, when they saw him stir up hatred and battles among Odin's children, they decided they must put a stop to it.

Down to earth came the gods all together, and caught the kicking, struggling Loki. How different he is now, thought Thor! For the thunder god had liked Loki in spite of his pranks. In the beginning his mischief had seemed just high spirits and love for adventure. He had once been a good companion. But no more.

The gods carried Loki to a huge dark cave at the end of the earth. They chained his hands and feet to rocks. On a ledge over his head they put a snake which dripped poison down upon the wicked god. There he was to stay till the end of the world.

But one was left who loved Loki. His wife was a young giantess. She walked the earth looking for her husband and calling his name. When she came to the

cave at the end of the earth where he was chained she rushed in to him and threw herself down beside him. But there was no way she could break the chains.

"I will catch the snake's poison in this cup before it falls upon your poor head," she cried. When the cup overflowed to fall upon Loki she would run and empty it, and quickly return to hold the cup over him again. Day after day she sat there catching the poison and easing her husband's suffering as much as she could.

In the meantime, a stranger knocked at the gates of Odin's palace. He was tall and strong, but his face was that of a child. He looked fresh and happy, with none of the worries and fears, none of the sadness of the gods. His hair was blown and tangled and there was a smudge upon his cheek.

"No one enters here uncombed and unwashed," said the doorkeeper. But the stranger only smiled and gently pushed him aside. On into Odin's palace he walked, and stood before the All-father.

"I am your newborn son," said the stranger in a sweet voice. "I am Vali, child of the spring. Only one day have I known, and I have not combed my hair or washed my face. First I must avenge Balder's death.

Hodur I seek. Like the spring, I will end his winter of dark sadness."

Odin smiled. It was as the prophetess had foretold. And he sent Vali into the dark forest outside of Asgard. There poor Hodur wandered lonely and afraid. There the blind god stumbled and groped his way waiting for the day when he would be sent to Hel's land, waiting to join the brother he had been tricked into killing.

Vali sent his arrow straight to the heart of Hodur. Balder was avenged! Now Hodur began his descent to the land of the dead.

Even so as each day passed the gods grew more sad and weary. They no longer had Balder to cheer them. Loki had spread so much evil in the world that everywhere they turned they met wickedness and unhappiness.

The sun and moon grew pale with horror. Their light barely shone through the thick mists that rose up from the land of the giants. Then the snow began to fall and the wind began to blow. The earth was covered with ice, and every few days it would shake and tremble as if it were falling to pieces. This was Loki tearing at his chains and twisting in pain because his wife had turned to empty the cup of poison.

The day came when Loki broke from his chains. Out of the cave he rushed and, with hate in his heart, called upon Hel and all the evil giants. He called out the snarling wolves and all hungry, angry beasts. Together they rushed to fight the great battle with the gods.

Heimdall raised his curved horn to his lips and its great blast rang throughout the world, making the earth tremble. When they heard the long-awaited sound, the gods gathered in Odin's hall. Their faces were stern and their voices quiet. The end was at hand.

The goddesses helped the gods put on their armor and handed them their weapons. Frigga placed Odin's golden helmet upon his head. And Sif handed Thor the magic gloves so that he could hurl his great hammer straight and true.

For the last time Odin rode his eight-legged horse at the head of his army. For the last time he led his warriors across the trembling rainbow bridge to the great battlefield that stretched a hundred miles each way.

Then there was a terrible crash. Down fell the great

ever green tree, ripping open the rocks and earth. With a great clap of thunder, a flaming sword tore the heavens apart. And the beautiful rainbow bridge was shattered and burst into flames.

Gods, giants and wolves struggled in the greatest battle the world had ever known. The great serpent, that had been the giants' cat, broke from its bonds and rushed into the battle. As the swords flashed and the battle cries rose to a thundering din, the flaming tongue of wild fire burned everywhere.

So all were destroyed — gods, giants, wolves, and serpent. And the fire purified all. Then the waves of the sea washed over and cooled the black and ruined world. It was as though Asgard, earth, and the giants' land had never been. There was no longer any evil nor any good.

Then were all the brave and good deeds of the gods for nothing? No, there was a better, purer world to come. Years of darkness passed. Then a small, faint star pricked its way through the gloom. It grew stronger and stronger until it became a rosy dawn. The waves rolled back into the sea. Little tender green blades sprang out of the blackened earth. Suddenly a bird's song trilled through the great stillness.

Then Odin's son Vali, the child of spring, appeared upon the earth. Who should follow him but the shining Balder, hand in hand with blind Hodur. Once again Balder's goodness would warm the world. And Hodur's darkness would bring the comfort of sleep.

It was as Odin had been told. The old gods gave their lives for a new and purer world. No price was too high for such beauty and peace.

Names and How to Pronounce Them

Asgard	*AS-gard*	home of the gods
Austri	*OS-tree*	the dwarf holding the east corner of the sky
Balder	*BOL-der*	god of sunlight and summer, son of Odin
Brock	*BROK*	the brave dwarf who stood up for his brother
Bure	*BOOR-ee*	the good giant who was found in the ice
Dvalin	*DVAHL-in*	the dwarf who made three gifts for Odin, and new hair for Sif
Freya	*FREYE-a*	goddess of love
Frigga	*FRIG-a*	mother of the gods, wife of Odin
Heimdall	*HEYEM-dahl*	watchman at the rainbow bridge
Hel	*HEL*	queen of the underworld
Hermod	*HER-mod*	messenger of the gods
Hodur	*HO-der*	god of winter, blind son of Odin
Idun	*EE-doon*	goddess of youth
Loki	*LO-kee*	evil demon of the gods
Mimir	*MEE-meer*	keeper of the well of wisdom
Nanna	*NAH-nah*	Balder's wife
Nordri	*NOR-dree*	the dwarf holding the north corner of the sky
Odin	*O-din*	chief of the gods, called Allfather
Roskva	*ROSK-vah*	peasant girl who went with Thor and Loki to the land of the giants
Sif	*SIF*	wife of Thor
Sindri	*SIN-dree*	greatest blacksmith of the dwarfs
Sleipner	*SLEYEP-ner*	Odin's eight-legged horse
Sudri	*SOO-dree*	the dwarf holding the south corner of the sky
Thialfi	*the-AHL-fee*	peasant boy who went with Thor and Loki to the land of giants
Thiassi	*the-AHS-see*	the storm giant
Thor	*THOR*	the thunder god, son of Odin
Vala	*VAHL-a*	prophetess in the land of the dead
Vali	*VAHL-ee*	god of spring, who brought peace to Hodur
Westri	*WES-tree*	the dwarf holding the west corner of the sky

132